11+

PRACTICE PAPERS

Set 1

Series editor Tracey Phelps,
the 11+ tutor with a

96% PASS RATE

Maths

English

Verbal Reasoning

Non-verbal Reasoning

Ages 10–11

Practice

SCHOLASTIC

Published in the UK by Scholastic Education, 2020

Book End, Range Road, Witney, Oxfordshire, OX29 0YD

A division of Scholastic Limited

London – New York – Toronto – Sydney – Auckland

Mexico City – New Delhi – Hong Kong

www.scholastic.co.uk

3 4 5 6 7 8 9   0 1 2 3 4 5 6 7 8 9

British Library Cataloguing-in-Publication Data

A catalogue record for this book is available from the British Library.

ISBN 978-1407-18373-2

Printed and bound by Ashford Colour Press

Papers used by Scholastic Limited are made from wood grown in sustainable forests.

Author

Tracey Phelps

Editorial team

Rachel Morgan, Suzanne Holloway, Audrey Stokes, Sarah Davies, Julia Roberts

Design team

Dipa Mistry

Illustration

Contents

About the CEM test

About the CEM test

The Centre for Evaluation and Monitoring (CEM) is one of the leading providers of the tests that grammar schools use in selecting students at 11+. The CEM test assesses a student's ability in Verbal Reasoning, Non-verbal Reasoning, English and Mathematics. Pupils typically take the CEM test at the start of Year 6.

Students answer multiple-choice questions and record their answers on a separate answer sheet. This answer sheet is then marked via OMR (Optical Mark Recognition) scanning technology.

The content and question type may vary slightly each year. The English and Verbal Reasoning components have included synonyms, antonyms, word associations, shuffled sentences, cloze (gap fill) passages and comprehension questions.

The Mathematics and Non-verbal Reasoning components span the Key Stage 2 Mathematics curriculum, with emphasis on worded problems. It is useful to note that the CEM test may include Mathematics topics which students will be introduced to in Year 6, such as ratio, proportion and probability.

The other main provider of such tests is GL Assessment. The GLA test assesses the same subjects as the CEM test and uses a multiple-choice format.

About this book

Scholastic 11+ Practice Papers for the CEM Test Ages 10–11 is part of the Pass Your 11+ series. The practice papers in this book have been designed to accurately reflect the format and style of the CEM test. The CEM test consists of two question papers, each of which contains elements of the four subjects being tested. Each test paper is divided into four or five sections with strict timings for each section. Students are not permitted to move backwards or forwards between the different sections during the test.

This book offers:

- Two full-length CEM-style papers to familiarise your child with the CEM test.
- Timings for each section to help your child become accustomed to working under time pressure.
- Multiple-choice questions to practise answering the types of question your child will meet in their CEM test.
- Multiple-choice answer sheets.
- Answers.
- Visit **https://shop.scholastic.co.uk/pass-your-11-plus/extras** for extended answers and additional answer sheets.

CEM-style
11+ Mixed Assessment
Practice Paper A

Information about this practice paper:

- The time allowed is given at the start of each section.

- The page number appears at the bottom of each page.

- The title of each section is provided on the top line of each page.

- Answers should be clearly marked in pencil on the answer sheets on pages 36 and 37, in the spaces provided. Additional answer sheets are available at **https://shop.scholastic.co.uk/pass-your-11-plus/extras**.

- Use the pages of the test to write your workings out.

- If you make a mistake, rub it out and insert your new answer.

- If you are not sure of an answer, choose the one you think would be best; do not leave it blank.

 You will see this symbol at the beginning of each section. It will tell you how many minutes are allowed for that section.

Blank page

Synonyms

Instructions

Select the word that has the SAME or SIMILAR meaning to the word on the left.
Mark your answer on the answer sheet (page 36) by choosing one of the options A–E.
There is only one right answer for each question.

Example 1

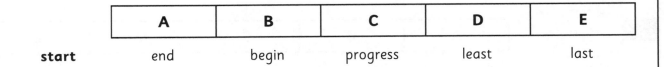

	A	B	C	D	E
start	end	begin	progress	least	last

The correct answer is:

> **B**

> begin

The answer, B, has been marked for you on the answer sheet.

Example 2

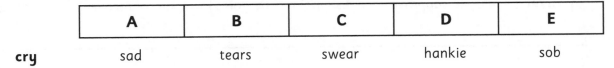

	A	B	C	D	E
cry	sad	tears	swear	hankie	sob

The correct answer is:

> **E**

> sob

Mark the box with the letter E on the answer sheet.

 You have 5 minutes for this section.

Synonyms

1

obtain

A	B	C	D	E
require	enquire	acquire	object	observe

2

completely

A	B	C	D	E
merely	entirely	nearly	widely	fairly

3

aim

A	B	C	D	E
dependence	confidence	assurance	intention	reliance

4

amount

A	B	C	D	E
quantity	quality	variety	mixture	measure

5

quarrel

A	B	C	D	E
disapprove	disappoint	disallow	discover	disagree

6

doubtful

A	B	C	D	E
unmistakable	uncertain	indisputable	inevitable	incredible

7

quicken

A	B	C	D	E
consolidate	accommodate	accelerate	invalidate	update

Synonyms

8

rapidly

A	B	C	D	E
absently	constantly	modestly	swiftly	strictly

9

comprehend

A	B	C	D	E
consider	estimate	explain	tolerate	understand

10

remarkable

A	B	C	D	E
reasonable	reliable	extraordinary	exciting	exhausting

11

distant

A	B	C	D	E
remote	private	removed	secret	relevant

12

repulsive

A	B	C	D	E
appealing	corrupt	stale	revolting	polluted

13

reveal

A	B	C	D	E
discover	disclose	disable	discard	dismiss

14

roam

A	B	C	D	E
sprint	dash	fly	skip	stray

Synonyms

15 **abrupt**

A	B	C	D	E
unexplained	unexplored	unfinished	unexpected	unplanned

16 **think**

A	B	C	D	E
comfort	consider	console	confirm	compose

17 **really**

A	B	C	D	E
simply	wholly	actually	merely	slightly

18 **entrance**

A	B	C	D	E
acceptance	introduction	allowance	assumption	admission

19 **terrified**

A	B	C	D	E
fearful	shy	worried	mean	horrid

20 **agitated**

A	B	C	D	E
serious	nervous	rigorous	vicious	callous

21 **enlarge**

A	B	C	D	E
elaborate	embellish	entwine	expect	expand

Synonyms

22

A	B	C	D	E
fretful	restful	fateful	helpful	hurtful

relaxing

23

A	B	C	D	E
nodding	yawning	sleeping	dreaming	soothing

slumbering

24

A	B	C	D	E
fictitious	adventurous	imaginative	faithful	doubtful

false

25

A	B	C	D	E
security	subsidy	custody	sanctuary	support

refuge

26

A	B	C	D	E
messy	sloppy	hasty	rickety	wobbly

rash

Comprehension

Instructions

Carefully read through the passage of writing. Then answer the questions that follow.
Mark your answer on the answer sheet (page 36) by choosing one of the options A–D.
Look at the examples below.

Example Passage

The boys went fishing by the river. They only caught one fish.

Example 1

Where did the boys go fishing?

A. By the river

B. In the pond

C. In the sea

D. By the lake

The correct answer is A, 'By the river'.

Find example 1 in the Comprehension section on the answer sheet.

The answer, A, has been marked for you.

Example 2

How many fish did they catch?

A. Fifteen

B. None

C. Plenty

D. One

The correct answer is D, 'One'.

Mark the box with letter D on the answer sheet for example 2.

 You have **14** minutes for this section.

Comprehension

Mary Wade

The latter part of the 18th century was a challenging time for Londoners. Soldiers returning home from the Anglo-French wars were looking for jobs that didn't exist and poverty was rife. Children – some as young as four years old – were sent out to earn extra money working as street-sweepers, costermongers, chimney sweeps, maids, shoe shiners and mudlarks. There was a sharp upsurge in crime as many people

5 were forced to steal in order to make ends meet. Punishments from the courts were severe; petty thieves were routinely handed the death penalty and London's gaols were bursting with prisoners awaiting their journey to the gallows. When the prisons simply couldn't pack in any more inmates, criminals were sent to the hulks – disused, dirty warships moored in the murky waters of the Thames at Woolwich.

Mary Wade was just ten years old when she was caught stealing some clothing from a seven-year-old

10 girl. She was convicted and sentenced to death. Immediately after her trial, she was taken from her mother and marched out of the Old Bailey to be thrown into gaol. Mary was never to see her mother again. Upon her arrival at Newgate Prison, Mary would have been chained and then led to the appropriate dungeon for her crime. She then would have been shackled to the floor along with up to 50 other women, all barely subsisting on stale bread and unclean water and all awaiting the same fate.

15 Conditions in prisons were harsh and the lack of food and hygiene meant that disease and illness spread quickly among the inmates. The cells were so dismal, damp and dirty that even physicians refused to enter the buildings.

On 16 March 1789, Mary Wade received the excellent news that the then monarch, King George III – in celebration of his recovery from insanity – had graciously pardoned all women prisoners awaiting

20 execution and had their sentences commuted to transportation. She would escape the hangman's noose in favour of boarding the *Lady Juliana* convict ship setting sail for Captain James Cook's newly discovered Australia.

The *Lady Juliana* set sail from London on 2 July 1789 and docked for eight weeks at Rio de Janeiro to take on supplies of coffee and sugar, before setting out on the next leg of its journey; the 50-day

25 trip across the Atlantic to Cape Town, in Southern Africa. Mary perhaps stood on the deck as they approached land and the majestic Table Mountain came into view.

At last, on 3 June 1790, almost a year after she had left England, Mary Wade, now 11 years old, arrived in Australia. Five women and two children had sadly perished during the passage. Mary was sent to a small, lush island, 1000 miles east of Sydney, Norfolk Island. It was here that Mary was to meet the

30 man she would soon marry: John Brooker. Brooker was also a convict who, just like his new bride, had been found guilty of stealing in England and had been transported a year previously on the Atlantic.

Having served their seven years, the pair were granted land in New South Wales on the Australian mainland. Mary and John went on to have 21 children and by 1822 they owned 62 acres of land which they farmed together.

35 At the age of 80, after having led a very successful life, Mary died one week before Christmas Day in 1859 and had well in excess of 300 descendants at the time of her demise. Thousands of Australians are descended from Mary Wade, perhaps the most famous of whom is the former Australian Prime Minister, Kevin Rudd.

Mary Wade's journey from street-sweeper to affluent and influential Australian landowner is probably

40 something that she could not have possibly imagined the day that she dared to steal a dress and a hat.

Comprehension

1   What did Mary steal from the younger child?

A. Some sweets

B. A bread roll

C. Some clothes

D. A purse

2   What was Mary's childhood occupation in London?

A. She was a costermonger.

B. She swept the roads and pavements.

C. She was a mudlark, dredging the Thames for things that might be valuable.

D. She polished wealthy people's shoes.

3   Where did Mary Wade stand trial for her crime?

A. Woolwich Crown Court

B. Shoreditch Magistrates Court

C. The Old Bailey

D. Westminster Crown Court

4   To which prison was Mary Wade taken after her sentence had been passed?

A. Pentonville Prison

B. Newgate Prison

C. Holloway Prison

D. The *Lady Juliana*

Comprehension

5 Which of the following words is another word for 'prisoner'?

A. Inmate

B. Primate

C. Reprobate

D. Roommate

6 Which of the following sentences could be used to describe Norfolk Island?

A. A sparsely populated island infested with predatory sharks in its surrounding waters

B. An island rich in beautiful flowers and trees

C. A remote, cold island full of convicted prisoners and lawlessness

D. An idyllic paradise island that is prone to typhoons and earthquakes

7 How many people died on the ship that carried Mary Wade to Australia?

A. Five

B. Two

C. Seven

D. None

8 On which date did Mary Brooker die?

A. 16 December 1859

B. 18 December 1859

C. 19 December 1859

D. 18 December 1833

Comprehension

9 Why was John Brooker on Norfolk Island?

A. He was an explorer and had discovered the island while on a voyage to find new lands.

B. He was transported to the island after having been found guilty of murder.

C. He was sent there after being convicted of theft.

D. He was part of the crew working on board the *Lady Juliana*.

10 Why was crime more common just after the cessation of the Anglo-French conflicts?

A. Because the police force hadn't been founded yet and people could simply get away with stealing.

B. Because unemployment was high and many people couldn't manage to feed their families without resorting to theft.

C. Because the population of London had risen, making it inevitable that the instances of crimes would increase.

D. Because soldiers returning home from the war were resorting to crime.

11 Which intrepid explorer had recently discovered Australia and claimed it as a British colony?

A. Christopher Columbus

B. Sir Francis Drake

C. Captain James Cook

D. Roald Amundsen

12 How long were Mary and John's sentences?

A. 21 years

B. 10 years

C. 5 years

D. 7 years

Comprehension

13   Where were prisoners sent to when the gaols were full?

    A. Newgate Prison

    B. Houses of correction in the countryside

    C. Floating prison ships on the river

    D. The gallows

---

14   From which debilitating illness was King George III cured in the late 1780s?

    A. Insanity

    B. Cholera

    C. Tuberculosis

    D. Consumption

---

15   Which body of professionals declined to visit London's prisons during the Georgian era?

    A. Judges

    B. Lawyers

    C. Doctors

    D. Teachers

---

16   Over which ocean did the *Lady Juliana* travel from South America to Africa?

    A. The Pacific Ocean

    B. The Indian Ocean

    C. The South Atlantic Ocean

    D. The Atlantic Ocean

Comprehension

17 Which one of the following statements is true?

A. Mary Wade was just ten years old when the *Lady Juliana* docked in Australia.

B. The current Australian Prime Minister is Kevin Rudd.

C. The *Lady Juliana* was moored at Cape Town for three months en route to Australia.

D. Sydney is situated to the west of Norfolk Island.

18 Which of the following statements is <u>not</u> true?

A. John Brooker travelled to Australia on the *Atlantic*.

B. It took over a year for the *Lady Juliana* to reach its destination.

C. Petty thieves were often handed the death sentence for their crimes.

D. The stunning Table Mountain is located at the southern tip of Africa.

19 '...to affluent and influential Australian landowner is probably something that she could not have possibly imagined'. What does the word 'affluent' mean in this context?

A. Prosperous

B. Important

C. Popular

D. Hard working

20 'She then would have been shackled to the floor along with up to 50 other women, all barely subsisting on stale bread and unclean water'. What does the phrase 'barely subsisting on' mean in this context?

A. Just managing to survive on

B. Being force fed

C. Feasting on

D. Sharing among them

Pictures 1

Instructions

Choose the picture which shows the top-down 2D view of the 3D picture on the left.

Example 1

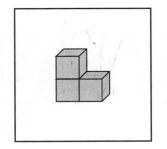 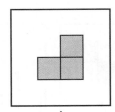 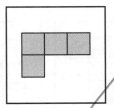 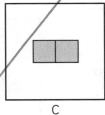 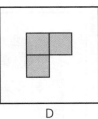

A   B   C   D

The answer to example 1 is C.

The answer C has been marked for you on the answer sheet (page 36).

Example 2

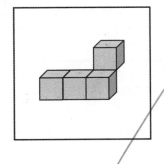 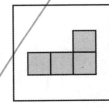 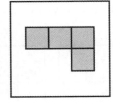 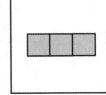 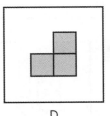

A   B   C   D

The answer to example 2 is A.

Mark the box with the letter A on the answer sheet.

 You have 9 minutes for this section.

Pictures 1

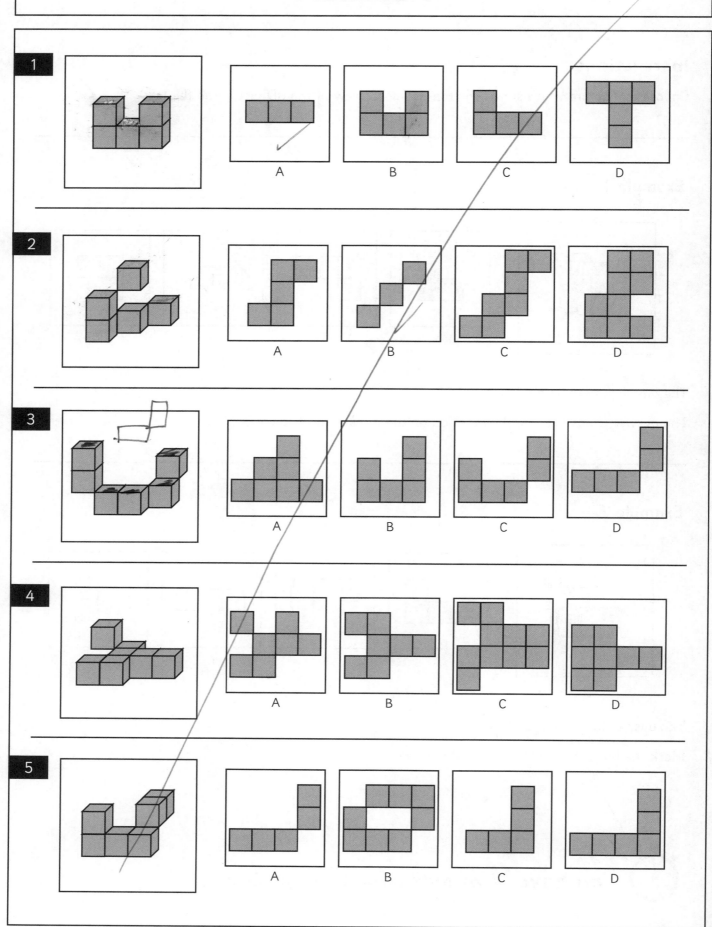

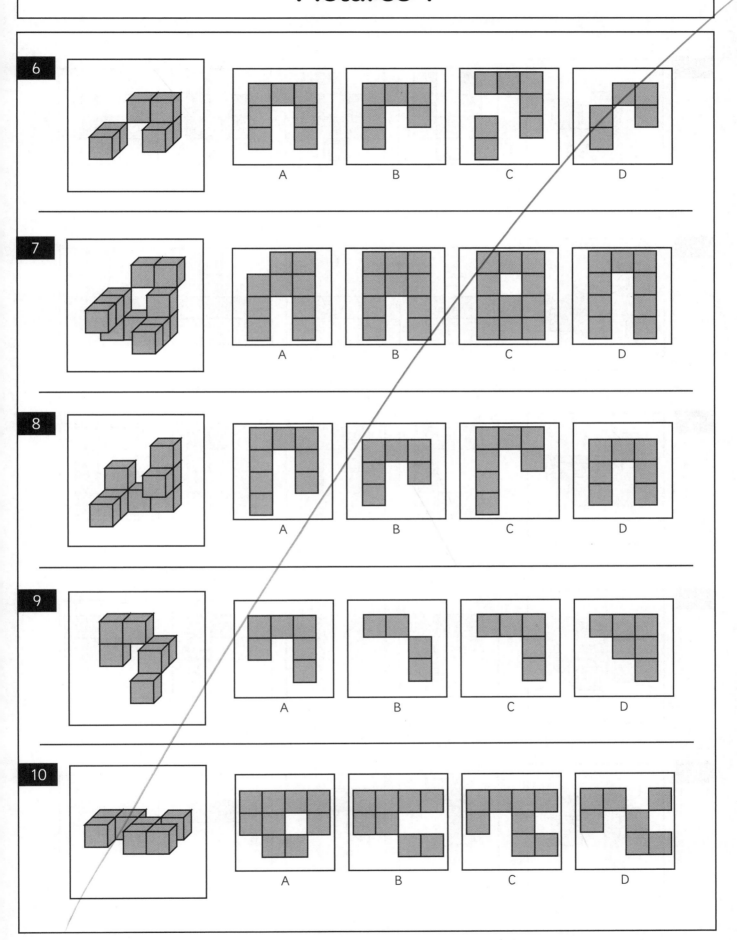

Pictures 1

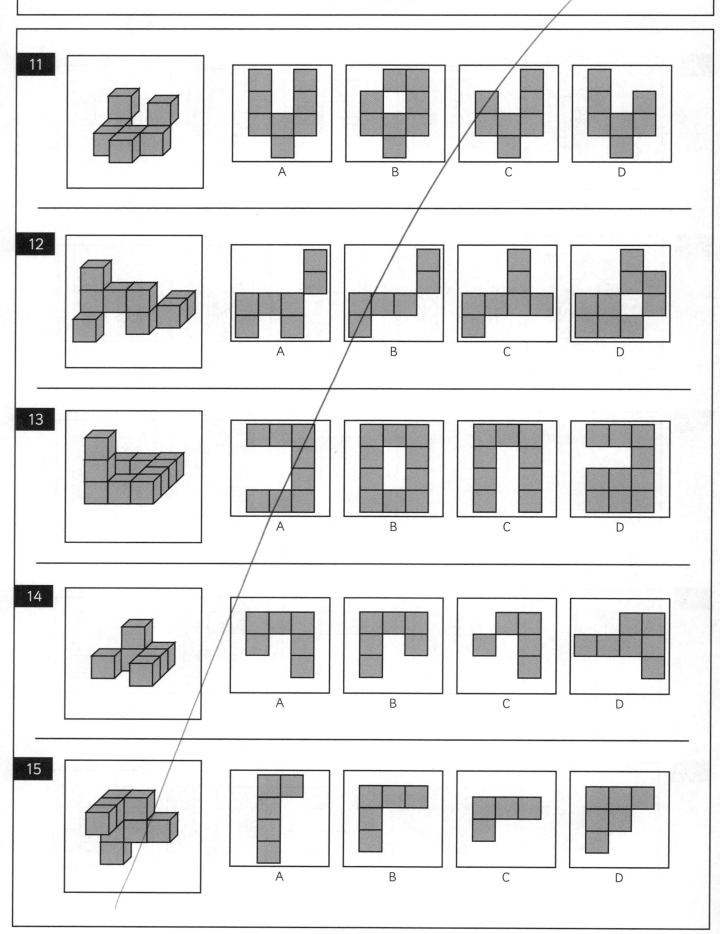

Pictures 1

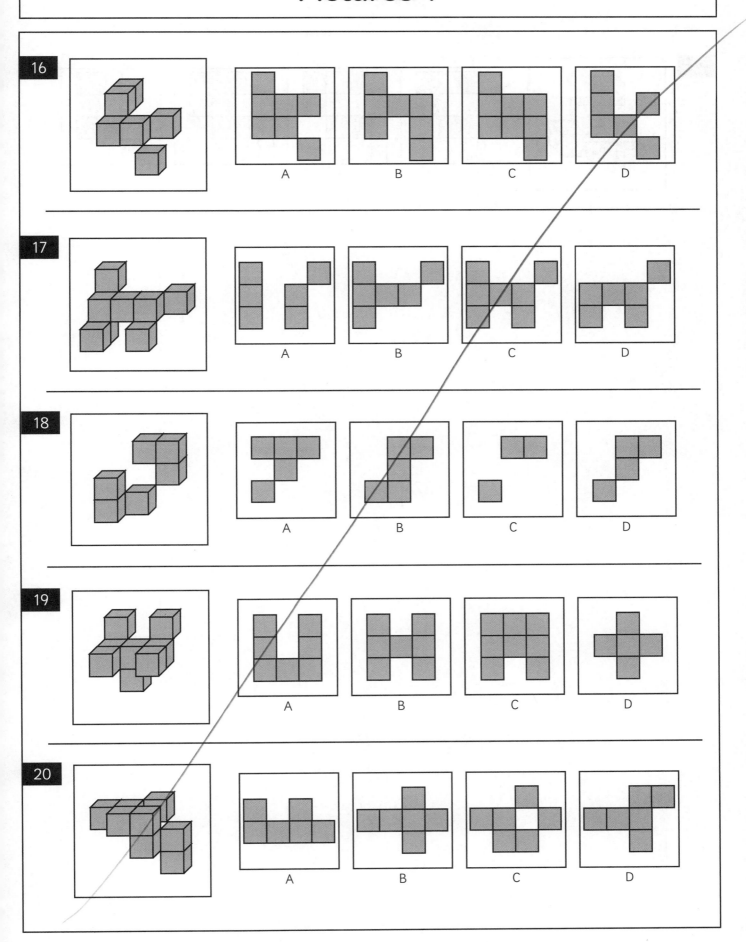

Pictures 1

21

A   B   C   D

Maths 1

Instructions

In this section, choose one option from A–E to answer the question. Mark your answer on the answer sheet (page 37) by choosing one of the options A–E. Look at the examples below.

Example 1

What is 14 + 38?

A	B	C	D	E
54	52	62	64	48

The answer is:

B
52

The answer, B, has been marked for you on the answer sheet.

Example 2

Which of the following numbers is a squared number greater than 64 and smaller than 100?

A	B	C	D	E
121	49	144	81	100

The answer is:

D
81

Mark the box with the letter D on the answer sheet.

 You have 12 minutes for this section.

Maths 1

1 A drinks bottle full of water weighs 1.2kg. Half the water is poured out and the new weight of the water bottle is 750g.

What is the mass of the drinks bottle when it is empty?

A	B	C	D	E
250g	275g	350g	325g	300g

2 Tom is raising money for charity. He counts up his old toys and finds that he doesn't play with 78 of them any more. He gives one third away to some friends.

He takes the remaining toys to the charity shop.

How many toys does Tom take to the charity shop?

A	B	C	D	E
48	50	52	54	56

3 Raj reads 32 pages of his new book in the afternoon. When he goes to bed he reads another 19 pages. Raj has now read one third of the book.

How many pages are there in the book?

A	B	C	D	E
51	153	102	141	162

4 Tessa catches a train from London to Reading at 11:10. The journey takes 50 minutes and then she waits 15 minutes for a second train to take her to Exeter. She arrives in Exeter at 14:40.

How long did Tessa's second train journey take?

A	B	C	D	E
2 hrs 40 mins	2 hrs 10 mins	1 hr 25 mins	2 hrs 25 mins	2 hrs 5 mins

Maths 1

5 A DIY shop is having a closing down sale. On the first day of the sale, 4212 tins of paint are sold and on the second day, 336 fewer tins of paint are sold.

How many tins of paint were sold in the first two days of the closing down sale?

A	B	C	D	E
8088	4548	8188	8424	7088

6 Ryan has £31.50 and his brother Sam has £27.10. Ryan agrees to give Sam some of his money so that the two boys have exactly the same amount each.

How much money does Ryan give to Sam?

A	B	C	D	E
£1.50	£2.20	£1.70	£2.25	£2.40

7 A cafe has 11 tables that can seat 4 people and 6 tables that seat 2 people.

How many customers will be eating in the cafe when all the tables are full of customers?

A	B	C	D	E
46	48	66	56	64

8 Three tins of cat food and two tins of dog food cost a total of £3.45.

Two tins of cat food and two tins of dog food cost a total of £2.70.

How much does one tin of dog food cost?

A	B	C	D	E
75p	65p	80p	45p	60p

Maths 1

9 How many degrees are there in the acute angle between the hands of an analogue clock when the time is showing exactly two o'clock?

A	B	C	D	E
15 degrees	60 degrees	75 degrees	45 degrees	55 degrees

10 Agata and Hattie share a cake between them. Agata eats half the cake and Hattie eats one quarter.

What percentage of the cake is left?

A	B	C	D	E
20%	15%	25%	17.5%	40%

11 First-class stamps cost 70p each and second-class stamps cost 61p each.

How much cheaper would it be to buy a dozen second-class stamps than to buy a dozen first-class stamps?

A	B	C	D	E
£1.80	£1.10	£1.08	£1.44	£1.96

12 Archie weighed 3.2kg when he was born. When he was weighed four weeks later, he had grown and now weighed 4.0kg.

What was the percentage increase in Archie's weight?

A	B	C	D	E
25%	20%	30%	35%	40%

13 A multi-storey car park has eight floors. Each floor can accommodate 56 cars, except for the ground floor, where there are 48 parking spaces.

How many cars will be parked in the car park when it is completely full?

A	B	C	D	E
496	480	506	430	440

Maths 1

14 Nasir takes 15 minutes to drive to work every morning and his office is situated seven miles from his house.

What is Nasir's average speed every morning?

A	B	C	D	E
40 mph	42 mph	21 mph	28 mph	35 mph

15 Zara has six 50p coins and two 20p coins.

She buys a book costing £2.99.

How much money does Zara have left?

A	B	C	D	E
39p	43p	41p	36p	45p

16 The mean (average) of three numbers is 9. The mode of the same three numbers is 6.

What is the largest of the three numbers?

A	B	C	D	E
15	12	9	6	18

17 Bianca's empty school backpack weighs 800g. She packs her school textbooks which weigh a total of 4.2kg and her pencil case which weighs 600g. She just manages to squeeze in her packed lunch which weighs 375g.

What is the mass of Bianca's backpack when it is full?

A	B	C	D	E
5.375kg	5.65g	6.175g	5.975kg	6.975kg

Maths 1

18 Olga's car uses eight litres of fuel every 50 kilometres.

How much fuel would her car use on a 225 kilometre trip to Manchester?

A	B	C	D	E
45 litres	36 litres	30 litres	35 litres	32 litres

19 Max is following a recipe for fisherman's pie. The recipe specifies 400g of salmon is needed to serve four people.

How many grams of salmon will be required in order to serve six people?

A	B	C	D	E
575g	750g	650g	900g	600g

20 The children in Mrs Naylor's class were asked if they would like to have the option of fish and chips on the school lunch menu. Two thirds of the children answered 'yes' and the remaining seven children answered 'no'.

How many children are there in Mrs Naylor's class?

A	B	C	D	E
28	32	18	21	25

21 Dr Harrison saw a total of 52 patients in her busy evening surgery and prescribed medicines for 25% of the patients.

How many of Dr Harrison's patients did not require a prescription?

A	B	C	D	E
13	28	39	21	42

Maths 2

Instructions

In this section, mark your answer on the answer sheet (page 37) by filling in the correct number. Look at the examples below.

Example 1

What is 18 minus 12?

The answer is 6 and has been marked for you on the answer sheet.

The number 6 is written as '06' in the top boxes and the corresponding digits '0' and '6' are marked in the boxes below.

O	6
[0]	[0]
[1]	[1]
[2]	[2]
[3]	[3]
[4]	[4]
[5]	[5]
[6]	[6]
[7]	[7]
[8]	[8]
[9]	[9]

Example 2

What is 18 × 4?

The answer is 72.

Mark the correct answer 72 on the answer sheet.

 You have **10** minutes for this section.

Maths 2

1   Martha has 54 stickers.

She gives $\frac{1}{6}$ of her stickers to her friend Sophie and $\frac{1}{5}$ of her remaining stickers to her cousin Emma.

How many stickers does Martha have left?

_____

2   A coach leaves Brighton with 42 passengers on board. A third of the passengers leave the coach at the first stop and six passengers get on the coach.

How many passengers are there on the coach after it has made its first stop?

_____

3   A flight travelling from London to Beijing is carrying 280 passengers. There are twice as many passengers in economy as there are in business class. There are twice as many business-class passengers as there are first-class passengers.

How many passengers are travelling in first class?

_____

4   Makena visits the school uniform shop and buys one blazer, two skirts and three shirts. Her bill totals £106.

Victoria visits the same shop and buys an identical blazer, two skirts and five shirts. Her bill amounts to £130.

How many shirts can be bought for £50?

Maths 2

5 There are three boxes inside a larger box.

The three boxes each have six much smaller boxes inside them.

How many boxes are there in total?

6 In a 'guess the number of sweets in a jar' competition, 120 children take part. $\frac{5}{8}$ guessed too high and $\frac{1}{4}$ guessed too low.

How many children were lucky enough to guess the correct number?

7 Freddie is reading a new library book.

He is able to read 5 pages in 12 minutes.

How many pages will Freddie be able to read in one hour?

8 David and Aisha spent an entire day fishing in the summer holidays.

Aisha caught twice as many fish as David and altogether they caught 24 fish.

How many fish did David catch?

Maths 2

9　The ferry from Portsmouth to the Isle of Wight can carry a maximum of 75 cars on each crossing.

How many crossings will be needed to transport 900 cars?

10　This year George's age is a multiple of nine.

Next year his age will be a multiple of five.

He is older than 30 and younger than 60 years old.

How old is George?

11　Sofie is replacing the tiles on her kitchen floor.

Her new square tiles have sides that measure 50cm.

Her kitchen floor measures 4 metres long and is 3 metres wide.

How many tiles does Sofie need to buy?

12　Millie's purse contains £3.52.

The coins are all 20p and 2p coins, in equal numbers.

How many coins are there in Millie's purse?

Blank page

Answer sheets

Student name:

Synonyms p.7

Examples:

| 1 | [A] | ~~[B]~~ | [C] | [D] | [E] |
| 2 | [A] | [B] | [C] | [D] | [E] |

Questions

1	[A]	[B]	[C]	[D]	[E]
2	[A]	[B]	[C]	[D]	[E]
3	[A]	[B]	[C]	[D]	[E]
4	[A]	[B]	[C]	[D]	[E]
5	[A]	[B]	[C]	[D]	[E]
6	[A]	[B]	[C]	[D]	[E]
7	[A]	[B]	[C]	[D]	[E]
8	[A]	[B]	[C]	[D]	[E]
9	[A]	[B]	[C]	[D]	[E]
10	[A]	[B]	[C]	[D]	[E]
11	[A]	[B]	[C]	[D]	[E]
12	[A]	[B]	[C]	[D]	[E]
13	[A]	[B]	[C]	[D]	[E]
14	[A]	[B]	[C]	[D]	[E]
15	[A]	[B]	[C]	[D]	[E]
16	[A]	[B]	[C]	[D]	[E]
17	[A]	[B]	[C]	[D]	[E]
18	[A]	[B]	[C]	[D]	[E]
19	[A]	[B]	[C]	[D]	[E]
20	[A]	[B]	[C]	[D]	[E]
21	[A]	[B]	[C]	[D]	[E]
22	[A]	[B]	[C]	[D]	[E]
23	[A]	[B]	[C]	[D]	[E]
24	[A]	[B]	[C]	[D]	[E]
25	[A]	[B]	[C]	[D]	[E]
26	[A]	[B]	[C]	[D]	[E]

Comprehension p.12

Examples:

| 1 | ~~[A]~~ | [B] | [C] | [D] |
| 2 | [A] | [B] | [C] | [D] |

Questions

1	[A]	[B]	[C]	[D]
2	[A]	[B]	[C]	[D]
3	[A]	[B]	[C]	[D]
4	[A]	[B]	[C]	[D]
5	[A]	[B]	[C]	[D]
6	[A]	[B]	[C]	[D]
7	[A]	[B]	[C]	[D]
8	[A]	[B]	[C]	[D]
9	[A]	[B]	[C]	[D]
10	[A]	[B]	[C]	[D]
11	[A]	[B]	[C]	[D]
12	[A]	[B]	[C]	[D]
13	[A]	[B]	[C]	[D]
14	[A]	[B]	[C]	[D]
15	[A]	[B]	[C]	[D]
16	[A]	[B]	[C]	[D]
17	[A]	[B]	[C]	[D]
18	[A]	[B]	[C]	[D]
19	[A]	[B]	[C]	[D]
20	[A]	[B]	[C]	[D]

Pictures 1 p.19

Examples:

| 1 | [A] | [B] | ~~[C]~~ | [D] |
| 2 | [A] | [B] | [C] | [D] |

Questions

1	[A]	[B]	[C]	[D]
2	[A]	[B]	[C]	[D]
3	[A]	[B]	[C]	[D]
4	[A]	[B]	[C]	[D]
5	[A]	[B]	[C]	[D]
6	[A]	[B]	[C]	[D]
7	[A]	[B]	[C]	[D]
8	[A]	[B]	[C]	[D]
9	[A]	[B]	[C]	[D]
10	[A]	[B]	[C]	[D]
11	[A]	[B]	[C]	[D]
12	[A]	[B]	[C]	[D]
13	[A]	[B]	[C]	[D]
14	[A]	[B]	[C]	[D]
15	[A]	[B]	[C]	[D]
16	[A]	[B]	[C]	[D]
17	[A]	[B]	[C]	[D]
18	[A]	[B]	[C]	[D]
19	[A]	[B]	[C]	[D]
20	[A]	[B]	[C]	[D]
21	[A]	[B]	[C]	[D]

Mixed Assessment Practice Paper A

Maths 1 p.25

Examples:

1	[A]	~~[B]~~	[C]	[D]	[E]
2	[A]	[B]	[C]	[D]	[E]

Questions

1	[A]	[B]	[C]	[D]	[E]
2	[A]	[B]	[C]	[D]	[E]
3	[A]	[B]	[C]	[D]	[E]
4	[A]	[B]	[C]	[D]	[E]
5	[A]	[B]	[C]	[D]	[E]
6	[A]	[B]	[C]	[D]	[E]
7	[A]	[B]	[C]	[D]	[E]
8	[A]	[B]	[C]	[D]	[E]
9	[A]	[B]	[C]	[D]	[E]
10	[A]	[B]	[C]	[D]	[E]
11	[A]	[B]	[C]	[D]	[E]
12	[A]	[B]	[C]	[D]	[E]
13	[A]	[B]	[C]	[D]	[E]
14	[A]	[B]	[C]	[D]	[E]
15	[A]	[B]	[C]	[D]	[E]
16	[A]	[B]	[C]	[D]	[E]
17	[A]	[B]	[C]	[D]	[E]
18	[A]	[B]	[C]	[D]	[E]
19	[A]	[B]	[C]	[D]	[E]
20	[A]	[B]	[C]	[D]	[E]
21	[A]	[B]	[C]	[D]	[E]

Maths 2 p.31

Examples:

1

0	6
~~[0]~~	[0]
[1]	[1]
[2]	[2]
[3]	[3]
[4]	[4]
[5]	[5]
[6]	~~[6]~~
[7]	[7]
[8]	[8]
[9]	[9]

2

[0]	[0]
[1]	[1]
[2]	[2]
[3]	[3]
[4]	[4]
[5]	[5]
[6]	[6]
[7]	[7]
[8]	[8]
[9]	[9]

Questions

1

[0]	[0]
[1]	[1]
[2]	[2]
[3]	[3]
[4]	[4]
[5]	[5]
[6]	[6]
[7]	[7]
[8]	[8]
[9]	[9]

4

[0]	[0]
[1]	[1]
[2]	[2]
[3]	[3]
[4]	[4]
[5]	[5]
[6]	[6]
[7]	[7]
[8]	[8]
[9]	[9]

7

[0]	[0]
[1]	[1]
[2]	[2]
[3]	[3]
[4]	[4]
[5]	[5]
[6]	[6]
[7]	[7]
[8]	[8]
[9]	[9]

10

[0]	[0]
[1]	[1]
[2]	[2]
[3]	[3]
[4]	[4]
[5]	[5]
[6]	[6]
[7]	[7]
[8]	[8]
[9]	[9]

2

[0]	[0]
[1]	[1]
[2]	[2]
[3]	[3]
[4]	[4]
[5]	[5]
[6]	[6]
[7]	[7]
[8]	[8]
[9]	[9]

5

[0]	[0]
[1]	[1]
[2]	[2]
[3]	[3]
[4]	[4]
[5]	[5]
[6]	[6]
[7]	[7]
[8]	[8]
[9]	[9]

8

[0]	[0]
[1]	[1]
[2]	[2]
[3]	[3]
[4]	[4]
[5]	[5]
[6]	[6]
[7]	[7]
[8]	[8]
[9]	[9]

11

[0]	[0]
[1]	[1]
[2]	[2]
[3]	[3]
[4]	[4]
[5]	[5]
[6]	[6]
[7]	[7]
[8]	[8]
[9]	[9]

3

[0]	[0]
[1]	[1]
[2]	[2]
[3]	[3]
[4]	[4]
[5]	[5]
[6]	[6]
[7]	[7]
[8]	[8]
[9]	[9]

6

[0]	[0]
[1]	[1]
[2]	[2]
[3]	[3]
[4]	[4]
[5]	[5]
[6]	[6]
[7]	[7]
[8]	[8]
[9]	[9]

9

[0]	[0]
[1]	[1]
[2]	[2]
[3]	[3]
[4]	[4]
[5]	[5]
[6]	[6]
[7]	[7]
[8]	[8]
[9]	[9]

12

[0]	[0]
[1]	[1]
[2]	[2]
[3]	[3]
[4]	[4]
[5]	[5]
[6]	[6]
[7]	[7]
[8]	[8]
[9]	[9]

Answers

Synonyms
p.7

1	C
2	B
3	D
4	A
5	E
6	B
7	C
8	D
9	E
10	C
11	A
12	D
13	B
14	E
15	D
16	B
17	C
18	E
19	A
20	B
21	E
22	B
23	C
24	A
25	D
26	C

Comprehension
p.13

1	C
2	B
3	C
4	B
5	A
6	B
7	C
8	B
9	C
10	B
11	C
12	D
13	C
14	A
15	C
16	D
17	D
18	B
19	A
20	A

Pictures 1
p.19

1	A
2	B
3	D
4	B
5	C
6	D
7	A
8	B
9	C
10	D
11	D
12	B
13	A
14	C
15	B
16	D
17	C
18	D
19	B
20	C
21	A

Maths 1
p.25

1	E
2	C
3	B
4	D
5	A
6	B
7	D
8	E
9	B
10	C
11	C
12	A
13	E
14	D
15	C
16	A
17	D
18	B
19	E
20	D
21	C

Maths 2
p.31

1	36
2	34
3	40
4	04
5	22
6	15
7	25
8	08
9	12
10	54
11	48
12	32

Extended answers
for Mixed Assessment Practice Paper A

Synonyms p.7

1	Both words mean 'to get'.
2	Both words mean 'fully'.
3	Both words mean 'goal'.
4	Both words mean 'how much of something'.
5	Both words mean 'to argue'.
6	Both words mean 'not certain'.
7	Both words mean 'to go faster'.
8	Both words mean 'quickly'.
9	Both words mean 'to understand'.
10	Both words mean 'out of the ordinary'.
11	Both words mean 'far off'.
12	Both words mean 'nasty'.
13	Both words mean 'to make known'.
14	Both words mean 'to walk without any fixed direction'.
15	Both words mean 'sudden'.
16	Both words mean 'to think'.
17	Both words mean 'genuinely'.
18	Both words mean 'entry'.
19	Both words mean 'frightened'.
20	Both words mean 'disturbed'.
21	Both words mean 'to make bigger'.
22	Both words mean 'calm'.
23	Both words mean 'dozing'.
24	Both words mean 'not true'.
25	Both words mean 'a safe place'.
26	Both words mean 'to do something in a hurry'.

Comprehension p.12

1	Line 10 – 'caught stealing some clothing'
2	Line 39 – 'Mary Wade's journey from street-sweeper'
3	Line 12 – 'marched out of the Old Bailey'
4	Line 13 – 'Upon her arrival at Newgate Prison'
5	Line 17 – 'spread quickly among the inmates.'
6	Line 29 – 'a small, lush island'
7	Line 28 – 'Five women and two children had sadly perished'
8	Lines 35 and 36 – Mary died one week before Christmas Day in 1859'
9	Lines 30 and 31 – 'Brooker…had been found guilty of stealing'
10	Line 2 – 'looking for jobs that didn't exist'
11	Line 22 – 'setting sail for Cook's newly discovered Australia.'
12	Line 32 – 'Having served their seven years'
13	Lines 7 and 8 – 'When the prisons simply couldn't pack in any more inmates, criminals were sent to the hulks – disused, dirty warships…'
14	Line 20 – 'in celebration of his recovery from insanity'
15	Lines 17 and 18 – 'physicians refused to enter the buildings.'
16	Lines 24 and 25 – '50-day trip across the Atlantic'
17	Line 29 – '1000 miles east of Sydney.'
18	Line 27 'At last, on 3 June 1790, almost a year after she had left England'
19	Affluent means 'wealthy' or 'prosperous'.
20	Line 15 – 'stale bread and unclean water…' This would imply that the prisoners were just managing to survive.

Extended answers
for Mixed Assessment Practice Paper A

Pictures 1 p.19

1	There is only one row of cubes, therefore answer must be A.
2	If you remove the top cubes it is clear that the answer must be B.
3	There are 3 cubes on the left and 2 cubes going backwards in a different row.
4	There are 2 cubes in the foreground which rules out C, a gap in the 2nd row which rules out D, 2 cubes on the right rules out A.
5	There are 3 cubes in the foreground and 2 further cubes behind the first row, answer must be C.
6	The 2 cubes on the left of the picture joined to the cube in the middle of the picture make the answer D.
7	The 3 cubes on the left of the picture rule out all answers except A.
8	The 3 cubes on the left of the picture rule out A and C. The 2 cubes on the right rule out D.
9	There are 3 cubes in the row and 3 cubes on the right of the picture making the answer C.
10	The cube at the right side of the picture rules out A, B and C.
11	The 2 cubes on the right of the picture rule out every option except D.
12	The 2 cubes on the right of the picture rule out C and D. There are 2 cubes in the foreground of A, so the answer is B.
13	There are 2 spaces behind the 3 cubes in the left of the picture, therefore the answer is A.
14	The 3 cubes on the right of the picture rule out B. The cube on the right rules out A. The 4 cubes in a row rule out D. The answer is C.
15	The 3 cubes on the left of the picture rule out A and C. D can also be ruled out.
16	The cube in isolation to the bottom right of the picture rules out B and C. The answer is D.
17	The 3 cubes to the centre of the picture rules out A. B can be ruled out because there is no 2nd cube to the front of the picture. D can be ruled out because there is no 3rd cube to the right.
18	The single cube at the left of the picture rules out B, C cannot be the answer as there are too many spaces. A cannot be correct as there are 3 cubes instead of 2. The answer is D.
19	C and D can be ruled out because they do not have a cube between the cubes at the top of the picture. A cannot be the answer as there is no cube in the middle row. The answer is B.
20	Answer is C, because it is the only option with a missing cube next to the cubes on the right of the picture.
21	Answer is A, because it is the only option to have 3 cubes joined at the edge in the bottom of the picture.

Extended answers
for Mixed Assessment Practice Paper A

Maths 1 p.25

1	Half the water must weigh 450g, therefore 750g – 450g = 300g
2	One third of 78 = 26, therefore Tom takes 78 – 26 toys to the charity shop; 78 – 26 = 52
3	One third of the book = 51 pages, therefore the whole book = 51 × 3 = 153
4	Tessa must arrive in Reading at 12:00 and leave at 12:15. Reading to Exeter takes 2 hours 25 minutes.
5	On the second day, 4212 – 336 tins are sold (3876) therefore the total will be (4212 + 3876) = 8088
6	Each boy needs to have £31.50 + £27.10, divided by 2 which equals £29.30. Ryan gives Sam £2.20.
7	11 × 4 = 44 plus 6 × 2 = 12 = 56
8	The difference in the bills is 1 tin of cat food and 75p which must be the cost of the cat food. Therefore £2.70 – £1.50 must = the cost of 2 tins of the dog food, 60p
9	There are 12 hours on an analogue clock and 360° divided by 6 equals 60°
10	One half plus one quarter = three quarters, therefore there is one quarter remaining $\frac{1}{4}$ = 25%
11	The difference in the price of each stamp is 9p, therefore the 2nd class stamps would be 9p × 12 cheaper
12	Archie has put on 800g, therefore he has gained 800g divided by 3200g which is 25%
13	7 × 56 = 392, plus 48 for the ground floor equals a total of 440
14	If it takes fifteen minutes to travel 7 miles, Tony can travel 28 miles per hour (7 × 4)
15	Zara must have £3.40. (6 × 50p = £3.00 + 2 × 20p = 40p) therefore she will have £3.40 – £2.99 left
16	If the mean of three numbers is 9, they must add up to 27. If the mode is 6, there must be two 6s. 6, 6 & 15
17	800g + 4200g + 600g + 375g + 5975g or 5.975kg
18	The car will use 4 litres every 25 miles. 225 miles ÷ 25 = 9.4 litres × 9 = 36
19	The recipe uses 100g of salmon per person, therefore Max will need 100g × 6 = 600g
20	Seven children must equal one third of the total, therefore the class must have 7 × 3 children
21	25% is equal to $\frac{1}{4}$, therefore $\frac{3}{4}$ did not require a prescription. $\frac{3}{4}$ of 52 equals 39

Extended answers
for Mixed Assessment Practice Paper A

Maths 2 p.31

1	One sixth of 54 equals 9, leaving Martha with 45. One fifth of 45 is 9, leaving Martha with 36
2	One third of 42 equals 14, leaving 28 on board. With the six new passengers, the total is 34
3	Use algebra. First class = x, business class = $2x$, first class = $4x$. $7x = 280$. $x = 40$
4	The difference in the bills is £24 and two shirts, therefore a shirt must cost £12 Four shirts can be bought for £50
5	1 large box + 3 boxes = 4 boxes. Plus 18 smaller boxes = 22
6	The fractions add up to $\frac{7}{8}$, therefore the remaining eighth would be correct. $\frac{1}{8}$ of 120 = 15
7	12 minutes x 5 = 1 hour, therefore Freddie can read 5 x 5 pages in 1 hour which equals 25 pages
8	Use algebra. Aisha's catch = $2x$, David's catch = x, therefore $3x = 24$. $x = 8$
9	900 ÷ by 75 = 12
10	Possible ages this year are 36, 45 or 54. Next year, 35, 40, 45, 50, 55. Must be 54 now
11	Sofie will need 8 tiles to cover the length of the floor and 6 tiles to cover the width. 8 × 6 = 48
12	Use algebra. £3.52 ÷ 11 = 32

CEM-style 11+ Mixed Assessment Practice Paper B

Information about this practice paper:

- The time allowed is given at the start of each section.

- The page number appears at the bottom of each page.

- The title of each section is provided on the top line of each page.

- Answers should be clearly marked in pencil on the answer sheets on pages 66 and 67, in the spaces provided. Additional answer sheets are available at **https://shop.scholastic.co.uk/pass-your-11-plus/extras**.

- Use the pages of the test to write your workings out.

- If you make a mistake, rub it out and insert your new answer.

- If you are not sure of an answer, choose the one you think would be best; do not leave it blank.

 You will see this symbol at the beginning of each section. It will tell you how many minutes are allowed for that section.

Blank page

Antonyms

Instructions

Select the word that has the OPPOSITE meaning to the word on the left.
Mark your answer on the answer sheet (page 66) by choosing one of the options A–E.

There is only one right answer for each question.

Example 1

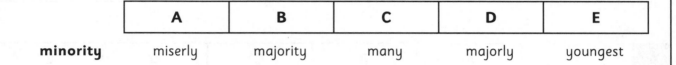

	A	B	C	D	E
minority	miserly	majority	many	majorly	youngest

The correct answer is:

> **B**
>
> majority

The answer, B, has been marked for you on the answer sheet.

Example 2

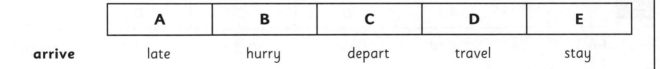

	A	B	C	D	E
arrive	late	hurry	depart	travel	stay

The correct answer is:

> **C**
>
> depart

Mark the box with the letter C on the answer sheet.

 You have **6** minutes for this section.

Antonyms

1   **found**

A	B	C	D	E
muddled	forlorn	mislaid	expired	waylaid

2   **moan**

A	B	C	D	E
reflect	rejoice	relapse	remark	request

3   **dryness**

A	B	C	D	E
mixture	mist	measure	moisture	pressure

4   **interesting**

A	B	C	D	E
frivolous	trivial	irrelevant	trifling	tedious

5   **loud**

A	B	C	D	E
muffled	bungled	stuffy	sultry	muggy

6   **real**

A	B	C	D	E
visionary	unrealistic	imaginary	legendary	ordinary

7   **orderly**

A	B	C	D	E
dirty	shabby	tacky	untidy	slimy

Antonyms

8   **neglect**

A	B	C	D	E
attraction	application	attention	ignorance	oversight

9   **calm**

A	B	C	D	E
flimsy	fuzzy	fussy	frilly	fidgety

10   **annoyance**

A	B	C	D	E
diversion	pleasure	entertainment	recreation	relaxation

11   **something**

A	B	C	D	E
nothing	nowhere	nobody	anything	anyhow

12   **nutritious**

A	B	C	D	E
harmful	hazardous	unsafe	unhelpful	unhealthy

13   **compulsory**

A	B	C	D	E
alternative	possible	required	optional	inconsistent

14   **clear**

A	B	C	D	E
unlikely	suspicious	vague	evident	unsettled

Antonyms

15   **alert**

A	B	C	D	E
unimportant	unintelligent	unobservant	unimpressed	uneducated

16   **modern**

A	B	C	D	E
dated	dingy	sloppy	musty	trendy

17   **quiet**

A	B	C	D	E
relaxed	restrained	rough	rude	rowdy

18   **assist**

A	B	C	D	E
construct	obstruct	instruct	destruct	observe

19   **onward**

A	B	C	D	E
beyond	before	behind	backward	ahead

20   **hide**

A	B	C	D	E
conceal	exhibit	mislead	exceed	examine

21   **cause**

A	B	C	D	E
issue	remainder	outcome	origin	outlay

Antonyms

22

A	B	C	D	E
outcome	outlook	mindset	result	outset

end

23

A	B	C	D	E
shameless	outrageous	notorious	obvious	hideous

reasonable

24

A	B	C	D	E
priced	quoted	estimated	owing	settled

paid

25

A	B	C	D	E
unbearable	unmistakable	unacceptable	unpredictable	unforgivable

satisfactory

26

A	B	C	D	E
press	pack	pull	proceed	plead

pause

Maths 3

Instructions

In this section you will be asked to mark your answers on the answer sheet (page 66) by choosing one of the options A–J shown at the top of each page.

A	B	C	D	E	F	G	H	I	J
72	75	56	60	28	52	26	48	80	90

Example 1

What is 14 + 38?

The answer is

F
52

The answer, F, has been marked for you on the answer sheet.

Example 2

What is 194 − 168?

The answer is

G
26

Mark the box with the letter G on the answer sheet.

 You have 15 minutes for this section.

Maths 3

A	B	C	D	E	F	G	H	I	J
6	27	15	3	7	12	18	21	25	9

The pie chart below shows the shoe sizes of the 60 children in Year 5.

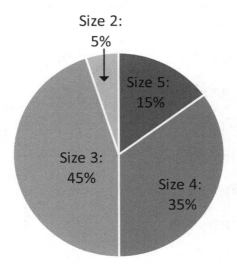

1   How many children take a size 2 shoe?

_____

2   How many children take size 3?

_____

3   How many more children take a size 3 than take a size 5?

_____

4   Two thirds of the children that take a size 4 are boys.

How many girls take a size 4?

Maths 3

A	B	C	D	E	F	G	H	I	J
131	255	449	245	459	757	231	417	349	747

The table below shows the number of customers entering a shop on a busy Friday just before Christmas.

9am–10am	410
10am–11am	188
11am–12pm	235
12pm–1pm	476
1pm–2pm	520
2pm–3pm	393
3pm–4pm	294
4pm–5pm	255
5pm–6pm	194

5   How many shoppers entered the shop between 4pm and 6pm?

_____

6   How many more customers visited the shop between the hours of 11am and 1pm than between 3pm and 4pm?

_____

7   One third of the customers that visited the shop between 2pm and 3pm were pensioners.

How many customers is this?

_____

8   Three quarters of the shoppers who visited the shop between the hours of 12am and 2pm were doing so during their lunch hour.

How many shoppers is this?

Maths 3

A	B	C	D	E	F	G	H	I	J
£9.60	£5.10	£10.80	£4.90	£7.20	£8.45	£5.30	£10.20	£9.00	£6.80

Cake	Cost each slice
Lemon drizzle cake	£1.65
Carrot cake	£1.90
Walnut cake	£1.70
Coconut cake	£1.40
Chocolate cake	£1.80

Emily is going to buy some cakes.

The price of each slice of cake is shown in the table above.

9 If Emily were to buy three slices of walnut cake, how much change would she receive if she pays with a £10 note?

_____

10 How much more expensive would it be for Emily to buy eight slices of carrot cake than to buy six slices of coconut cake?

_____

11 The patisserie has a special offer on boxes of 12 slices of cake. Emily can buy a dozen slices of any cake for a 50% discount.

How much would a box containing 12 slices of chocolate cake cost?

_____

12 How much would it cost if Emily were to buy one slice of each cake?

Maths 3

A	B	C	D	E	F	G	H	I	J
53 mins	55 mins	47 mins	61 mins	59 mins	70 mins	46 mins	67 mins	75 mins	81 mins

Below is a timetable giving details of morning trains from Cardiff to Reading.

Cardiff Central	08:43	09:03	09:23	09:43
Newport	09:13	09:33	—	10:13
Bristol	—	09:51	—	—
Swindon	—	—	09:47	—
Marlborough	09:42	10:03	10:22	10:42
Newbury	09:53	10:14	10:33	10:53
Reading	10:08	10:24	10:45	11:08

13 How many minutes does the fastest train take to travel from Cardiff Central to Reading?

14 How many minutes does the 09:23 service take to travel between Cardiff Central and Marlborough?

15 If you were to board the 09:13 service at Newport, how many minutes would pass before the train arrived at Reading?

16 If you were to catch the 09:47 train from Swindon, how long would it take to travel to Newbury?

Maths 3

A	B	C	D	E	F	G	H	I	J
65	33	68	13	21	26	15	39	19	70

A group of children went on a field trip to Wales.

There were 70 seats on the coach and after all the children and teachers had boarded the coach there was just one empty seat.

There were four adults on the trip.

The ratio of boys to girls was 2:3.

A third of the girls forgot to take a packed lunch.

Seven of the boys forgot to take any spending money with them.

17 How many children went on the field trip?

_____

18 How many girls were there on the coach?

_____

19 How many boys remembered to take some spending money with them?

_____

20 How many of the girls forgot to take a packed lunch?

Instructions

Look at the sequence of pictures on the left.
Two pictures are missing and are shown by a question mark.
Pick two pictures from A–F on the right that best complete the sequence.
Mark your answers on the answer sheet (page 67) by choosing from the options A–F.

Examples 1 and 2

The answer to example 1 is B.

The answer, B, has been marked for you on the answer sheet.

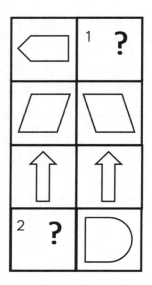

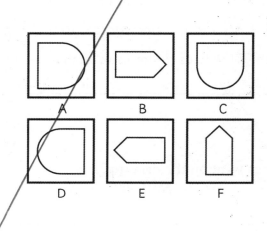

The answer to example 2 is D.
Mark the correct answer D on the answer sheet.

 You have **11** minutes for this section.

Pictures 2

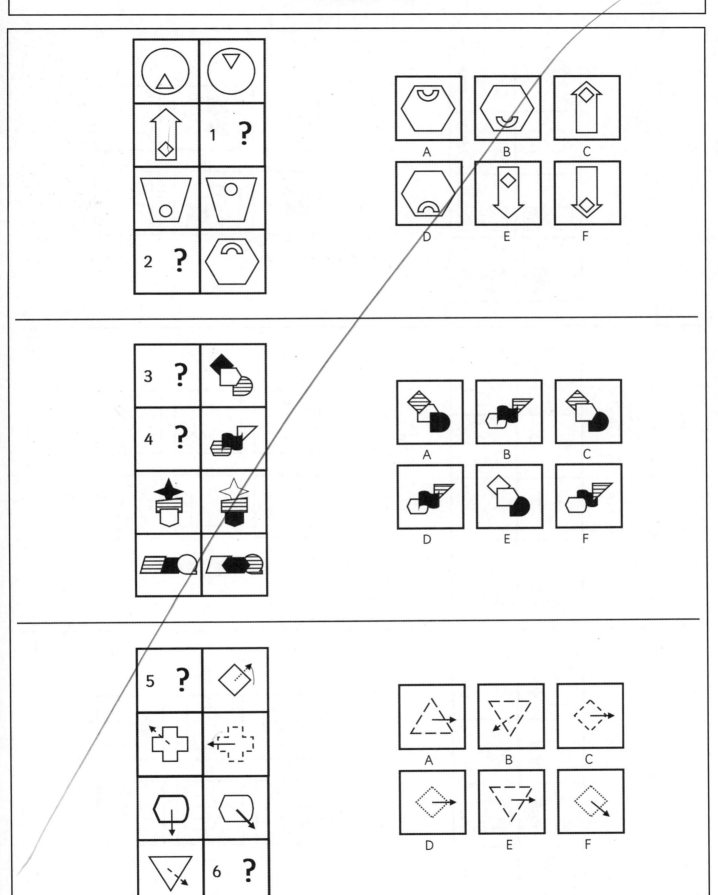

Pictures 2

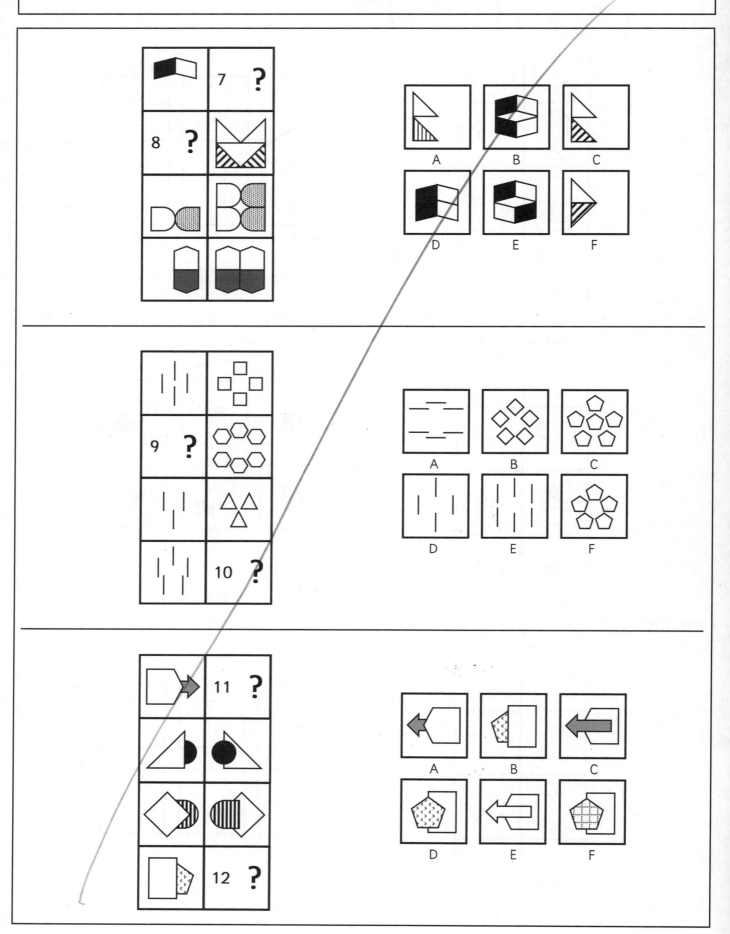

Pictures 2

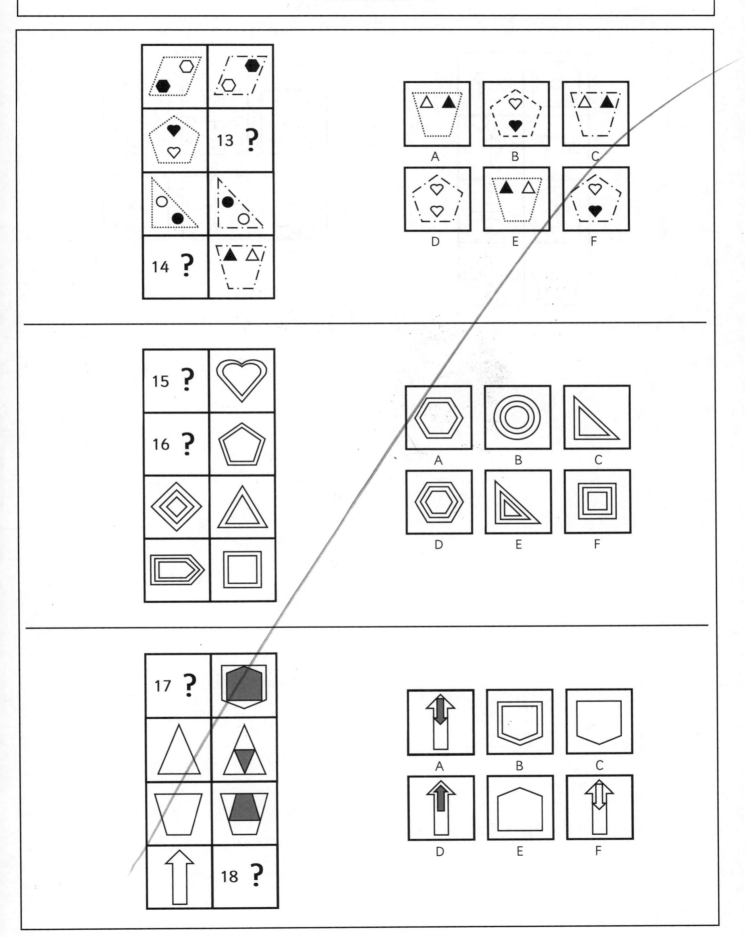

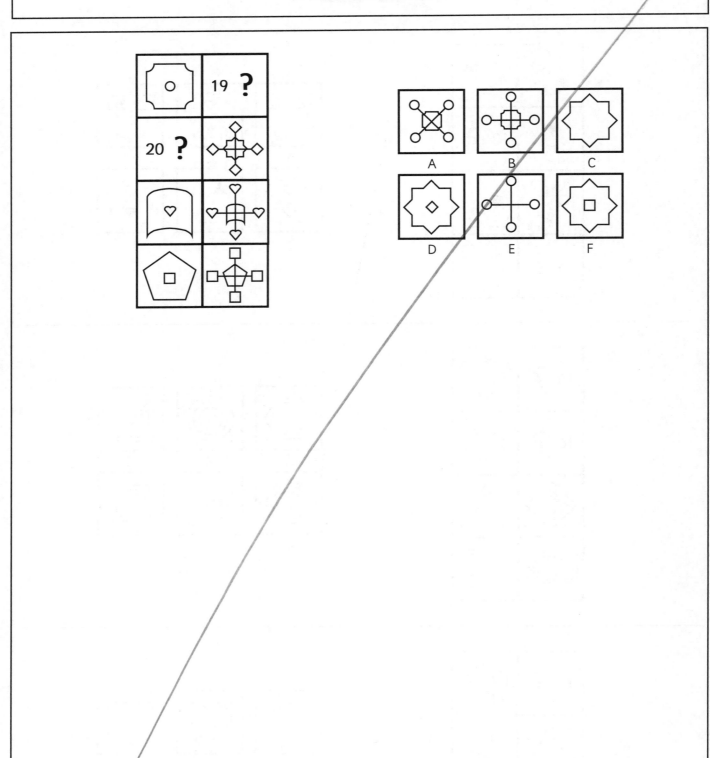

Cloze

Instructions

In the following passages, some of the words are missing. Please complete each passage by selecting the words from the options A–J. For each question, choose one word A–J and mark this on the answer sheet (page 67).

Each word can only be used once.

Example passage

A	B	C	D	E	F	G	H
glittered	majestic	ready	carved	throne	spun	adorn	sceptre

It was the night before the young 16-year-old prince was to be crowned king. He had gone to

bed early to rest, and lay there looking at all the things (Example **1**) for him to wear the next

morning. There was a robe of finely (Example **2**) gold, hand-stitched with beautiful patterns.

Example 1

The answer to example 1 is C, as the sentence should read:
It was the night before the young 16-year-old prince was to be crowned king. He had gone to
bed early to rest, and lay there looking at all the things <u>ready</u> for him to wear the next morning.

The answer, C, has been marked for you on the answer sheet.

Example 2

The answer to example 2 is F, as the sentence should read:
There was a robe of finely <u>spun</u> gold, hand-stitched with beautiful patterns.

Mark the box with the letter F on the answer sheet.

 You have **7** minutes for this section.

Cloze

Passage 1

A	B	C	D	E	F	G	H	I	J
lifting	riches	talented	sympathetic	experience	finish	uphill	level	decides	promises

Many (Question 1) young footballers dream of (Question 2) the Premier League trophy as the captain of their favourite team. But it's something that few will ever (Question 3). For most, it's an (Question 4) road to the fame and (Question 5) that a career in professional football (Question 6). A few make it to the top (Question 7); most don't.

Passage 2

A	B	C	D	E	F	G	H	I	J
pressures	sitting	hope	greatest	watching	sacrifice	years	national	leagues	convince

During the (Question 8) of playing in school teams, local (Question 9) and at local, district and county levels, talented youngsters (Question 10) to be spotted. A professional scout could be (Question 11) at any time. But scouts aren't just looking for the (Question 12) goal-scorers. Scouts understand the (Question 13) of a football career. Talent is important, but it's not enough to (Question 14) the scout of a player's potential.

Passage 3

A	B	C	D	E	F	G	H	I	J
recommends	finalises	finds	stiffens	system	club	guarantees	decides	skills	decisions

First, the scout (Question 15) a promising player. Next the scout (Question 16) the player to a professional team's academy. But it's a highly competitive (Question 17) with no (Question 18). At each level, players refine their (Question 19) but the competition (Question 20) too, and most football academy students will never become professionals.

Shuffled sentences

Instructions

Look at the examples. All the words form a sentence with one word left over. Select the word that does NOT belong in the sentence. Choose only one word for each sentence.

Mark your answer on the answer sheet (page 67) by choosing the letter, A–H, of the correct word.

Example 1

A	B	C	D	E	F	G	H
the	by	aeroplane	delayed	was	minutes	stopped	thirty

The sentence is:

D	B	C	F	E	A	H
the	aeroplane	was	delayed	by	thirty	minutes

So the leftover word is:

G
stopped

The answer, G, has been marked for you on the answer sheet.

Example 2

A	B	C	D	E	F	G	H
able	to	trainers	Yasmine	run	very	quickly	is

The sentence is:

D	H	A	B	E	F	G
Yasmine	is	able	to	run	very	quickly

So the left over word is:

C
only

Mark the box with the letter C on the answer sheet.

 You have **8** minutes for this section.

Shuffled sentences

1

A	B	C	D	E	F	G	H
were	and	the	blue	by	walls	painted	white

2

A	B	C	D	E	F	G	H
kept	open	the	Claire	day	all	windows	for

3

A	B	C	D	E	F	G	H
tyre	car	and	the	a	hit	tree	swerved

4

A	B	C	D	E	F	G	H
for	boiled	drink	Tony	kettle	have	the	a

5

A	B	C	D	E	F	G	H
a	on	sewed	his	button	shirt	thought	Matteo

6

A	B	C	D	E	F	G	H
made	rain	match	slippery	heavy	the	very	pitch

7

A	B	C	D	E	F	G	H
the	journey	Dave	due	late	to	was	roadworks

Shuffled sentences

8

A	B	C	D	E	F	G	H
turn	oven	forgot	Arjun	on	the	made	to

9

A	B	C	D	E	F	G	H
an	four	were	involved	road	in	vehicles	accident

10

A	B	C	D	E	F	G	H
the	Sarah	football	selected	team	was	for	hoped

11

A	B	C	D	E	F	G	H
cruise	of	cost	sailed	the	pounds	thousands	luxury

12

A	B	C	D	E	F	G	H
some	Rosie	awkward	on	the	spilled	carpet	tea

13

A	B	C	D	E	F	G	H
clock	at	past	the	three	after	stopped	ten

14

A	B	C	D	E	F	G	H
welcome	host	guests	gave	a	we	warm	our

Answer sheets

Student name:

Antonyms p.45

Examples:

| 1 | [A] | [B] | [C] | [D] | [E] |
| 2 | [A] | [B] | [C] | [D] | [E] |

Questions

1	[A]	[B]	[C]	[D]	[E]
2	[A]	[B]	[C]	[D]	[E]
3	[A]	[B]	[C]	[D]	[E]
4	[A]	[B]	[C]	[D]	[E]
5	[A]	[B]	[C]	[D]	[E]
6	[A]	[B]	[C]	[D]	[E]
7	[A]	[B]	[C]	[D]	[E]
8	[A]	[B]	[C]	[D]	[E]
9	[A]	[B]	[C]	[D]	[E]
10	[A]	[B]	[C]	[D]	[E]
11	[A]	[B]	[C]	[D]	[E]
12	[A]	[B]	[C]	[D]	[E]
13	[A]	[B]	[C]	[D]	[E]
14	[A]	[B]	[C]	[D]	[E]
15	[A]	[B]	[C]	[D]	[E]
16	[A]	[B]	[C]	[D]	[E]
17	[A]	[B]	[C]	[D]	[E]
18	[A]	[B]	[C]	[D]	[E]
19	[A]	[B]	[C]	[D]	[E]
20	[A]	[B]	[C]	[D]	[E]
21	[A]	[B]	[C]	[D]	[E]
22	[A]	[B]	[C]	[D]	[E]
23	[A]	[B]	[C]	[D]	[E]
24	[A]	[B]	[C]	[D]	[E]
25	[A]	[B]	[C]	[D]	[E]
26	[A]	[B]	[C]	[D]	[E]

Maths 3 p.50

Examples:

| 1 | [A] | [B] | [C] | [D] | [E] | [F] | [G] | [H] | [I] | [J] |
| 2 | [A] | [B] | [C] | [D] | [E] | [F] | [G] | [H] | [I] | [J] |

Questions

1	[A]	[B]	[C]	[D]	[E]	[F]	[G]	[H]	[I]	[J]
2	[A]	[B]	[C]	[D]	[E]	[F]	[G]	[H]	[I]	[J]
3	[A]	[B]	[C]	[D]	[E]	[F]	[G]	[H]	[I]	[J]
4	[A]	[B]	[C]	[D]	[E]	[F]	[G]	[H]	[I]	[J]
5	[A]	[B]	[C]	[D]	[E]	[F]	[G]	[H]	[I]	[J]
6	[A]	[B]	[C]	[D]	[E]	[F]	[G]	[H]	[I]	[J]
7	[A]	[B]	[C]	[D]	[E]	[F]	[G]	[H]	[I]	[J]
8	[A]	[B]	[C]	[D]	[E]	[F]	[G]	[H]	[I]	[J]
9	[A]	[B]	[C]	[D]	[E]	[F]	[G]	[H]	[I]	[J]
10	[A]	[B]	[C]	[D]	[E]	[F]	[G]	[H]	[I]	[J]
11	[A]	[B]	[C]	[D]	[E]	[F]	[G]	[H]	[I]	[J]
12	[A]	[B]	[C]	[D]	[E]	[F]	[G]	[H]	[I]	[J]
13	[A]	[B]	[C]	[D]	[E]	[F]	[G]	[H]	[I]	[J]
14	[A]	[B]	[C]	[D]	[E]	[F]	[G]	[H]	[I]	[J]
15	[A]	[B]	[C]	[D]	[E]	[F]	[G]	[H]	[I]	[J]
16	[A]	[B]	[C]	[D]	[E]	[F]	[G]	[H]	[I]	[J]
17	[A]	[B]	[C]	[D]	[E]	[F]	[G]	[H]	[I]	[J]
18	[A]	[B]	[C]	[D]	[E]	[F]	[G]	[H]	[I]	[J]
19	[A]	[B]	[C]	[D]	[E]	[F]	[G]	[H]	[I]	[J]
20	[A]	[B]	[C]	[D]	[E]	[F]	[G]	[H]	[I]	[J]

Pictures 2 p.56

Examples:

1	[A]	~~[B]~~	[C]	[D]	[E]	[F]
2	[A]	[B]	[C]	[D]	[E]	[F]

Questions

1	[A]	[B]	[C]	[D]	[E]	[F]
2	[A]	[B]	[C]	[D]	[E]	[F]
3	[A]	[B]	[C]	[D]	[E]	[F]
4	[A]	[B]	[C]	[D]	[E]	[F]
5	[A]	[B]	[C]	[D]	[E]	[F]
6	[A]	[B]	[C]	[D]	[E]	[F]
7	[A]	[B]	[C]	[D]	[E]	[F]
8	[A]	[B]	[C]	[D]	[E]	[F]
9	[A]	[B]	[C]	[D]	[E]	[F]
10	[A]	[B]	[C]	[D]	[E]	[F]
11	[A]	[B]	[C]	[D]	[E]	[F]
12	[A]	[B]	[C]	[D]	[E]	[F]
13	[A]	[B]	[C]	[D]	[E]	[F]
14	[A]	[B]	[C]	[D]	[E]	[F]
15	[A]	[B]	[C]	[D]	[E]	[F]
16	[A]	[B]	[C]	[D]	[E]	[F]
17	[A]	[B]	[C]	[D]	[E]	[F]
18	[A]	[B]	[C]	[D]	[E]	[F]
19	[A]	[B]	[C]	[D]	[E]	[F]
20	[A]	[B]	[C]	[D]	[E]	[F]

Cloze p.61

Examples:

1	[A]	[B]	~~[C]~~	[D]	[E]	[F]	[G]	[H]	[I]	[J]
2	[A]	[B]	[C]	[D]	[E]	[F]	[G]	[H]	[I]	[J]

Questions

1	[A]	[B]	[C]	[D]	[E]	[F]	[G]	[H]	[I]	[J]
2	[A]	[B]	[C]	[D]	[E]	[F]	[G]	[H]	[I]	[J]
3	[A]	[B]	[C]	[D]	[E]	[F]	[G]	[H]	[I]	[J]
4	[A]	[B]	[C]	[D]	[E]	[F]	[G]	[H]	[I]	[J]
5	[A]	[B]	[C]	[D]	[E]	[F]	[G]	[H]	[I]	[J]
6	[A]	[B]	[C]	[D]	[E]	[F]	[G]	[H]	[I]	[J]
7	[A]	[B]	[C]	[D]	[E]	[F]	[G]	[H]	[I]	[J]
8	[A]	[B]	[C]	[D]	[E]	[F]	[G]	[H]	[I]	[J]
9	[A]	[B]	[C]	[D]	[E]	[F]	[G]	[H]	[I]	[J]
10	[A]	[B]	[C]	[D]	[E]	[F]	[G]	[H]	[I]	[J]
11	[A]	[B]	[C]	[D]	[E]	[F]	[G]	[H]	[I]	[J]
12	[A]	[B]	[C]	[D]	[E]	[F]	[G]	[H]	[I]	[J]
13	[A]	[B]	[C]	[D]	[E]	[F]	[G]	[H]	[I]	[J]
14	[A]	[B]	[C]	[D]	[E]	[F]	[G]	[H]	[I]	[J]
15	[A]	[B]	[C]	[D]	[E]	[F]	[G]	[H]	[I]	[J]
16	[A]	[B]	[C]	[D]	[E]	[F]	[G]	[H]	[I]	[J]
17	[A]	[B]	[C]	[D]	[E]	[F]	[G]	[H]	[I]	[J]
18	[A]	[B]	[C]	[D]	[E]	[F]	[G]	[H]	[I]	[J]
19	[A]	[B]	[C]	[D]	[E]	[F]	[G]	[H]	[I]	[J]
20	[A]	[B]	[C]	[D]	[E]	[F]	[G]	[H]	[I]	[J]

Shuffled sentences p.63

Examples:

1	[A]	[B]	[C]	[D]	[E]	[F]	~~[G]~~	[H]
2	[A]	[B]	[C]	[D]	[E]	[F]	[G]	[H]

Questions

1	[A]	[B]	[C]	[D]	[E]	[F]	[G]	[H]
2	[A]	[B]	[C]	[D]	[E]	[F]	[G]	[H]
3	[A]	[B]	[C]	[D]	[E]	[F]	[G]	[H]
4	[A]	[B]	[C]	[D]	[E]	[F]	[G]	[H]
5	[A]	[B]	[C]	[D]	[E]	[F]	[G]	[H]
6	[A]	[B]	[C]	[D]	[E]	[F]	[G]	[H]
7	[A]	[B]	[C]	[D]	[E]	[F]	[G]	[H]

8	[A]	[B]	[C]	[D]	[E]	[F]	[G]	[H]
9	[A]	[B]	[C]	[D]	[E]	[F]	[G]	[H]
10	[A]	[B]	[C]	[D]	[E]	[F]	[G]	[H]
11	[A]	[B]	[C]	[D]	[E]	[F]	[G]	[H]
12	[A]	[B]	[C]	[D]	[E]	[F]	[G]	[H]
13	[A]	[B]	[C]	[D]	[E]	[F]	[G]	[H]
14	[A]	[B]	[C]	[D]	[E]	[F]	[G]	[H]

Answers

Antonyms p.45

1	C
2	B
3	D
4	E
5	A
6	C
7	D
8	C
9	E
10	B
11	A
12	E
13	D
14	C
15	C
16	A
17	E
18	B
19	D
20	B
21	C
22	E
23	B
24	D
25	C
26	D

Maths 3 p.50

1	D
2	B
3	G
4	E
5	C
6	H
7	A
8	J
9	D
10	J
11	C
12	F
13	J
14	E
15	B
16	G
17	A
18	H
19	I
20	D

Pictures 2 p.56

1	C
2	B
3	A
4	F
5	D
6	E
7	B
8	C
9	E
10	F
11	C
12	D
13	F
14	A
15	E
16	D
17	C
18	A
19	B
20	D

Cloze p.61

1	C
2	A
3	E
4	G
5	B
6	J
7	H
8	G
9	I
10	C
11	E
12	D
13	A
14	J
15	C
16	A
17	E
18	G
19	I
20	D

Shuffled sentences p.63

1	E
2	H
3	A
4	F
5	G
6	C
7	B
8	G
9	E
10	H
11	D
12	C
13	F
14	B

Mixed Assessment Practice Paper B

Extended answers
for Mixed Assessment Practice Paper B

Antonyms p.45

1	found means 'discovered', therefore the antonym is 'mislaid'
2	moan means 'to complain', therefore the antonym is 'rejoice'
3	dryness means 'a lack of moisture', therefore the antonym is 'moisture'
4	interesting means 'not boring or tedious', therefore the antonym is 'tedious'
5	loud means 'noisy', therefore the antonym is 'muffled' as it means 'quiet'
6	real means 'genuine', therefore the antonym is 'imaginary' as in 'just in your imagination'
7	orderly means 'tidy', therefore the antonym is 'untidy'
8	neglect means 'inattention', therefore the antonym is 'attention'
9	calm means 'still', therefore the antonym is 'fidgety'
10	annoyance means 'displeasure', therefore the antonym is 'pleasure'
11	something means 'an object or thing', therefore the antonym is 'nothing'
12	nutritious means 'healthy', therefore the antonym is 'unhealthy'
13	compulsory means 'not optional', therefore the antonym is 'optional'
14	clear means 'obvious', therefore the antonym is 'vague'
15	alert means 'observant', therefore the antonym is 'unobservant'
16	modern means 'up to date', therefore the antonym is 'dated'
17	quiet means 'hushed', therefore the antonym is 'rowdy'
18	assist means 'to help', therefore the antonym is 'obstruct'
19	onward means 'going forward', therefore the antonym is 'backward'
20	hide means 'to conceal', therefore the antonym is 'exhibit'
21	cause means 'the start of something', therefore the antonym is 'outcome'
22	end means 'the finish of something', therefore the antonym is 'outset'
23	reasonable means 'sensible', therefore the antonym is 'outrageous'
24	paid means 'a debt has been settled', therefore the antonym is 'owing'
25	satisfactory means 'acceptable', therefore the antonym is 'unacceptable'
26	pause means 'to stop', therefore the antonym is 'proceed'

Extended answers
for Mixed Assessment Practice Paper B

Maths 3 p.50

1	Size 2 = 5% of 60, which is 3
2	Size 3 is best found by multiplying the number of size 2s by 9, equalling 27
3	Size 3 is 27 as above. Size 5 will be size 2 × 3 = 9. 27 − 9 = 18
4	Size 4 total will be size 2 × 7 = 21. One third of 21 equals 7
5	255 + 194 = 449
6	Between 11am and 1pm is 235 + 476 = 711 − 294 from 3pm to 4pm = 417
7	One third of 393 equals 131
8	Total visitors between 12am and 2pm equals 476 + 520 (996) Three quarters of 996 equals 747
9	£1.70 × 3 = £5.10. Change would be £10.00 − £5.10 which is £4.90
10	8 slices of carrot cake (£1.90 x 8) − 6 slices coconut cake (£1.40 x 6) £15.20 - £8.40 = £6.80
11	12 slices of chocolate cake would cost 12 x £1.80 (£21.60) 50% of £21.60 = £10.80
12	£1.65 + £1.90 + £1.70 + £1.40 + £1.80 = £8.45
13	Train 2 is the quickest, taking 81 minutes
14	09:23 to 10:22 is 37 minutes + 22 minutes = 59 minutes
15	09:13 to 10:08 is 47 minutes + 8 minutes = 55 minutes
16	09:47 to 10:33 is 13 minutes + 33 minutes = 46 minutes
17	If there were 70 seats on the coach with one spare seat and 4 adults, there must have been 65
18	If the ratio of boys to girls was 2:3, there must have been 39 girls
19	If there were 39 girls, there must have been 26 boys. 26 − 7 = 19
20	If there were 39 girls there must have been 13 who forgot to take a packed lunch

Pictures 2 p.56

1 & 2	Inside shape is inverted therefore answers are C & B
3 & 4	Middle shape moves from background to foreground and shading reversed on outer shapes therefore answers are A & F
5 & 6	Shapes remain the same except for outline, arrow rotates 90° anti-clockwise, D & E
7 & 8	Shape is duplicated, therefore answers are B & C
9 & 10	Number of lines equals number of sides in the shapes, therefore E & F
11 & 12	Shapes are flipped horizontally and changed from foreground to background, C & D
13 & 14	Outlines change from dotted to dashed, inner shapes shading transposed, F & A
15 & 16	Number of sides in the shapes lessens by 1, therefore E & D
17 & 18	Smaller, inverted shape is added, therefore C & A
19 & 20	Outer shape becomes smaller, inner shape reproduced x 4, therefore B & D

Extended answers
for Mixed Assessment Practice Paper B

Cloze passage 1 p.61

Many <u>talented</u> young footballers dream of <u>lifting</u> the Premier League trophy as the captain of their favourite team. But it's something that few will ever <u>experience</u>. For most, it's an <u>uphill</u> road to the fame and <u>riches</u> that a career in professional football <u>promises</u>. A few make it to the top <u>level</u>; most don't.

Cloze passage 2 p.61

During the <u>years</u> of playing in school teams, local <u>leagues</u> and at local, district and county levels, talented youngsters <u>hope</u> to be spotted. A professional scout could be <u>watching</u> at any time. But scouts aren't just looking for the <u>greatest</u> goal-scorers. Scouts understand the <u>pressures</u> of a football career. Talent is important, but it's not enough to <u>convince</u> the scout of a player's potential.

Cloze passage 3 p.61

First, the scout <u>finds</u> a promising player. Next the scout <u>recommends</u> the player to a professional team's academy. But it's a highly competitive <u>system</u> with no <u>guarantees</u>. At each level, players refine their <u>skills</u> but the competition <u>stiffens</u> too, and most football academy students will never become professionals.

Shuffled sentences p.63

1	the walls were painted blue and white
2	Claire kept the windows open all day
3	the car swerved and hit a tree
4	Tony boiled the kettle for a drink
5	Matteo sewed a button on his shirt
6	heavy rain made the pitch very slippery
7	Dave was late due to the roadworks
8	Arjun forgot to turn the oven on
9	four vehicles were involved in an accident
10	Sarah was selected for the football team
11	the luxury cruise cost thousands of pounds
12	Rosie spilled some tea on the carpet
13	the clock stopped at ten past three
14	we gave our guests a warm welcome

 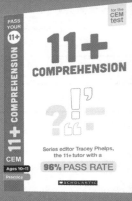